Maxine's CHRISTMAS CAROL

Illustrated by
John Wagner

Written by
Bill Gray
and Dan Taylor

Designed by
Terry O'Reagan

www.hallmark.com
www.shoebox.com

Published in the United States of America
by Hallmark Cards, Inc.

ISBN: 0-87529-803-6

PRINTED IN U.S.A.

lunk! A dart landed squarely on the nose of the smiling Santa face thumbtacked to the bulletin board in Maxine's office. "That oughta get me a good spot on the Naughty List," Maxine chuckled as she prepared to fire again. A noisemaker blasting over the office intercom broke her concentration, and the errant dart sailed through her open office door.

Rob, a friendly co-worker, poked his head through her door and asked, "Comin' to the office Christmas party, Maxine? It's starting right now!"

"Ho, ho, no way," Maxine responded.

"Have you been throwing darts at jolly old St. Nick?"

"I tried slushballs, but they kept melting before I could heave 'em."

Rob laughed good-naturedly. "Maxine, you're almost as crabby as Marlene, that big pain in the office who used to work here."

Maxine glanced toward a framed photograph showing Marlene hosing down the rest of the staff at a company picnic.

axine, who takes advantage of everything, took advantage of the long afternoon off. She stopped in at her neighborhood coffee shop, The Coffee Cat.

"Well, nothing says holiday to me like a festive nog-achino," Broderick said as he sipped from a tall paper cup. "Unless it's 'Santa's Little Helper.' It has triple the caffeine. One taste and you'll be up on the housetop."

On her way home, Maxine stopped in at the Lundquists' Bite 'n' Burp convenience store. Roy and Doris stood behind the counter, almost bursting from holiday happiness (or was it that last bag of pork rinds?). Maxine walked up with two packages of frozen burritos.

"Merry Christmas, Maxine!" the perky pair bubbled in unison.

"Anything to go with those burritos?" asked Doris. "May we recommend our pine-scented air freshener?"

"It's like a tiny Christmas tree for your car," Roy added gleefully.

"Or how about some Frosty's Frozen Onion Rings?" Doris suggested.

"Eat 'em or make a brown, greasy wreath," Roy interjected.

"Just bag the burritos. I gotta go," Maxine said.

"Doin' some last-minute gift shopping?" Doris wondered.

"All my shopping is last-minute. But it doesn't matter. I only shop for the ones I really like, me and my dog Floyd."

Maxine left the cuddly couple and drove home.

Floyd was nestled all snug by the fireplace with visions of bacon-wrapped cocktail weenies dancing in his head. He was startled awake by Maxine's voice bursting through the front door.

"Let's go for a walk, Floyd," Maxine called out. "Time for you to leave a holiday greeting on the neighbor's front lawn." Floyd darted through the doggie door and onto the frozen driveway.

Maxine and her faithful companion had only walked a few feet down her snowy sidewalk when a lightly packed snowball tapped her on the shoulder. She heard giggling and turned to see Billy, a little boy from down the street.

"Billy," Maxine said with mock sternness, "don't you know you shouldn't throw snowballs at people like that?" Billy stopped laughing, and his eyes began to grow wide until Maxine added, "You should throw them like this!"

Floyd tossed a snowball that Maxine expertly caught in one hand. Assuming a pitcher's stance, Maxine shook off an imaginary signal as Billy looked on with delight. She shook off a second signal before firing a fastball that whapped dead center into a mailbox across the street.

"Cool!" Billy exclaimed with admiration.

illy paused long enough to summon his courage and then asked a question.

"Maxine, can you come to our house for Christmas dinner tomorrow?"

"Ah, Christmas dinner, the perfect combination of noisy kids, annoying relatives, and questionable turkey gravy. You're barkin' up the wrong Christmas tree, kid."

"I even made you a present myself," Billy added softly.

"Look, why don't you take a long slide down a short hill. I told you I'm not coming."

As Maxine trudged into the house, Floyd looked back with sympathy toward the disappointed little boy.

Passing last Halloween's jack-o'-lantern still on the porch, Floyd yelped as the dried-up face let out a low moan.

"Okay, Floyd, now we lock the door, turn off the porch light, burrow in for twenty-four hours, and this whole Christmas thing blows over for another year," Maxine said.

Moments later she had settled into the recliner for a long winter's funk with a half-eaten burrito in one hand and a TV remote in the other. Every single channel was showing *It's a Wonderful Life,* including *Es Una Vida Maravillosa* on the Spanish station.

"Can you believe it, Floyd? Fifty-two channels and not a single Kung Fu movie?" Maxine asked irritably. Floyd, who was already asleep, didn't hear. In a short time, Maxine joined him in a winter slumberland.

s the grandfather clock chimed twelve times, a ghostly echoing voice filled the room.

"Maxine...Maxine...Maxine..."

Floyd jerked awake to see a ghostly figure hovering in midair.

Floyd nervously nudged his owner awake. Maxine's eyes popped open to see Marlene right in front of her.

"Oh, look," Maxine said calmly, "one of the Macy's parade floats broke loose."

"Oh, Maxine," the ghost droned. "In life you knew me as Marlene, the world's grouchiest office worker."

"Right," Maxine answered. "You're the one who was always tying up the line with personal phone calls while I was trying to make personal phone calls. So, you're still dead?"

"Listen to me, Maxine. Before this night is through, you will be visited by three ghosts. Heed their words and change your grumpy ways, or you will share my fate for all eternity."

As mysteriously as she had appeared, Marlene disappeared.

"You know, Floyd," Maxine said, "some people don't know how to stay dead."

ust then they heard loud thumping sounds coming from the attic. "Man, Floyd, the mice are gaining weight," Maxine remarked.

A pair of ethereal feet in clunky platform shoes drifted down through the ceiling, followed by the miniskirted form of a transparent teenager.

"Are you, like, Maxine?" the Valley ghost asked.

"Are you, like, the first ghost?" Maxine responded.

"Like, hel-loooo! Transparent? Floating? Came through the ceiling? I'm Tiffani, the ghost of Christmas past."

"Aren't you a little wet behind the pierced ears to be the ghost of Christmas past?"

"What can I say," Tiffani chirped. "I just totally love retro! And you know what's so-oo-oo retro? The past! And that's where we're going! Grab hold of my enchanted tennis bracelet, and we're on our way!"

In less time than it takes to run a credit check on your daddy's charge card, Tiffani, Maxine, and Floyd found themselves in a small town many, many years in the past.

"Hey, this looks like..." Maxine began.

"Right," Tiffani interrupted. "It's the town where you grew up. Let's check in on you when you were just a little crabette."

"Great," Maxine replied, "it'll be fun to see myself in the pre-droop years."

hen Tiffani flipped her hair, the trio found themselves transported to an upstairs bedroom where a very young Maxine was sitting on the bed with her kitty.

"Oh, Scarlett, this has been the best Christmas," cried little Maxine with delight. "I'm so glad I made gifts for everyone. I think they really loved them." Scarlett meowed in agreement, and little Maxine noticed that her kitty's milk dish was empty. "Why, you're all out of milk. I'll run down to the kitchen and get you some more."

From their perch on the headboard, Tiffani said, "Like, tear clouds forming, you were such a sweetie."

"I was clueless," Maxine groused.

As little Maxine skipped happily down the stairs, she could hear adult voices coming from the living room.

"Well, what did everyone think of Maxine's homemade gifts?" Uncle Fred chuckled.

"This ashtray's an insult to butts," answered Uncle George, and loud laughter filled the room.

Aunt Martha chimed in, "This pot holder will come in very handy, unless I want to pick up something hot."

"And I think there's a misspelling on this dish towel," Grandma said, "unless she meant to say 'Bless This Hose.'" Laughter erupted and rang through the house. Undetected, a tearful little Maxine ran back to her room and the comfort of her cat.

"Scarlett, you and I can just spend Christmas by ourselves--we don't need them." Reaching into her toy box, she defiantly put on a pair of sunglasses. "And they're not going to see me cry."

"So this is when the Grumpy Train left the station, huh?" Tiffani said quietly. "Oh, Tannenbummer."

With a beep of Tiffani's pager, Maxine and Floyd found themselves alone, back in the living room.

As Maxine and Floyd looked at each other with "Did that really happen?" expressions, they heard the sound of gentle sitar music coming from the television. They turned their heads to see a mysterious mystic hovering in the lotus position a few inches above the set.

"Oh, great," Maxine said, "another dumb thing on TV."

"I am the ghost of Christmas present," the ghostly guru intoned gently. "I am here to help you find the true aura of the holidays that radiates from within all of us. I will show you the way if you but give me your hand."

Instantly they found themselves in Billy's house, where a Christmas party was under way. Broderick, the Lundquists, and lots of other happy revelers shared the Christmas spirit.

"This is a great party," Billy's dad said to his wife.

"Right," she replied, "because Maxine's not here."

'She's so rude she could be French," Broderick replied.

"The poor dear just doesn't like anything about Christmas," Doris said, shaking her head sadly.

"Not even gingerbread with squirty cheese?" an astonished Roy asked.

axine, Floyd, and the guru took it all in from a corner of the room. He spoke serenely to Maxine, "Don't you think it's time for you to get back in touch with your inner child? That need to be loved?"

"By this bunch?" Maxine snapped. "If you ask me, they can all kiss a frozen flagpole."

"Ahh," the guru responded, "we're not here for them, we're here for Billy."

The crowd parted, and Maxine saw Billy standing at the front window, nose pressed against the glass.

"I told you she wouldn't come," Billy's mom said to her son, laying a hand on his shoulder.

"But I really, really wanted to give her my present."

"It's too bad," Billy's dad said soothingly. "I was hoping this year would be different."

"I don't know why you two keep inviting her," Billy's mom said. "She's so mean she curdles the eggnog."

Billy defended her. "Oh, she's not so bad, she just gets a little grouchy at Christmas."

"Calling Maxine a little grouchy is like calling your room a little messy," Billy's mom said.

A n invisible force slowly pulled Maxine, Floyd, and their ghostly companion from the room. As they drifted out over the lawn and back toward Maxine's house, the guru said, "For this family to truly enjoy Christmas without you is like a wind chime that has one ding-y thing and no other ding-y thing for the first ding-y thing to ding against."

Maxine leaned toward Floyd, rolled her eyes, and said, "There's definitely a ding-y thing here, but it's not a wind chime."

"For you to achieve true happiness, little cricket of crabbiness," the seer spoke, "you must give of yourself. And you don't want Billy to have a terrible Christmas, do you--like the one you had when you were a child?"

"He'll get over it," Maxine shot back.

*T*he guru spoke in an otherworld-weary tone. "I have nothing more to teach you, my pilgrim of poutiness. Click your bunny slippers together, and repeat after me, 'There's no place like ommm, there's no place like ommm, there's no place like...'"

Maxine and Floyd found themselves back in the safety of their living room. Maxine spoke to Floyd, "Well, at least the night can't get any weirder."

The room exploded into nearly blinding light surrounding the easy chair. The light began to levitate the recliner, Maxine, and Floyd into the air.

"You know," Maxine remarked, "this could be the first time I've ever been wrong."

Maxine and Floyd, along with the easy chair, were pulled by the light into the control center of an enormous spaceship. Generators hummed, lights blinked, holographic images flickered across large screens, and before them stood three silvery-skinned aliens.

"Merry Christmas," they said in tinny, high-pitched voices.

"We are the Grays."

"Don't tell me," Maxine guessed. "You overgrown silverfish are the ghosts of Christmas future?"

One of the Grays spoke. "Our mission is to show you the consequences of your failure to embrace the spirit of what you earthlings refer to as Christmas. Brace yourself for time travel."

efore she could respond, they zoomed up into space and back to earth at blinding speed. Suddenly the viewing screen filled with an image of colonial America, where people in powdered wigs emerged from horse-drawn carriages.

"Whoops," said a Gray, "I accidentally put it in reverse."

With an exasperated sigh, another Gray pushed a button on a panel, and they repeated the procedure at the speed of light.

In a nanosecond, they were hovering outside a tall building. On a large screen inside the ship, there appeared a luxurious executive office. An intense young man was yelling into the phone.

"I don't care if it's the first, fifth, or twelfth day of Christmas--I need that right now!"
As Maxine watched in the eerie blue light of the spaceship, she asked, "Is that my Billy?"
On the screen, a young woman popped her head into Billy's office.
"What?" Billy screamed.
"It's Christmas Eve," the woman said timidly. "I thought I might leave a little bit early."
"It's not Christmas Eve in the Far East," Billy said.
"What have you got against Christmas?"
"It was ruined for me a long time ago by a crabby old lady."

Maxine stood silently, deep in thought. Finally she said, "Is there any way I can change the future?"

"Do you have an XK1 relativity modulator transformer?" one of the Grays asked.

"No, not on me."

The Grays exchanged glances, and one of them said, "Okay, then, you will have to modify your behavior."

"You mean I'll have to be...nice?"

The aliens gave each other high threes, and one of them said to Maxine, "Are you ready to go back?"

"Make it so, Short Stuff. But first let me ask you something."

"Roswell?" They answered in unison, "That wasn't us."

*M*axine's and Floyd's atoms were scattered and rematerialized on the stairs where Billy was sitting with chin on hands, slumping sadly, and staring absently at the party taking place around him. Maxine leaned over and whispered into Billy's ear, "I showed up, where's my present?"

Billy turned and looked at her with a big smile. He jumped up and ran to his room at the top of the stairs, returning almost immediately with a clumsily wrapped package.

"I knew you'd come!" he shouted. "I made this just for you!"

"Homemade gifts are the best kind," Maxine said.

Maxine and Floyd tore off the wrapping paper to reveal a rock with a snowman painted on it.

"Billy, you've got talent." Maxine said with a smile.

Billy's mom looked in from the kitchen and called, "Dinner's ready in five minutes!"

After a festive evening, Maxine gave Billy a final holiday hug. As she and Floyd crunched across the snow-covered lawn, tiny flakes floated down from above. "Guess that wasn't so bad," Maxine mused.

"I'll give 'em Christmas. That still leaves me 364 days to be as crabby as I want."

Other SHOEBOX Characters
in MAXINE'S CHRISTMAS CAROL
(in order or appearance):

BRODERICK Illustrated by Peter Martin
ROY AND DORIS LUNDQUIST Illustrated by Payton Kelly
TIFFANI Illustrated by Maria O'Keefe
GURU GUY Illustrated by Mark Franzke
THE GRAYS Illustrated by Gary Pratt